Chimney Coi ... Tales

By Joan Heard

Best wishes
Joan Heard

The newcomers to the town ask the older generation of Stratton folk to remember...........

Stratton Folk

They ask us to remember!

Do the folk who live here now,

Who've lived in yonder Cottage,

The 'What?', the 'Why?', the 'How?'

Once we were the young folk, hearing the school bell ring,

Now we're the old folk - remembering,

Of names long forgotten - writ in the Book of Stratton Time,

The craftsmen and the tradesfolk.

And when the church bells chime,

We will open memory's door

For the folk who lived here before.

Emily

The Autumn sunlight filtered through the stained glass windows of Stratton Church leaving a path of many coloured lights across the slate floor. It was cold in the Church and, as Emily knelt, she drew her cloak closer around her body.

She was a stranger here in this Cornish village; one who spoke in her own way and not as they did. She remembered her people in faraway Swindon, so poor that they were forced to place her 'in service'.

The long journey on the coach, down through the rolling countryside until arriving at Bude she heard for the first time the sound of the sea as the surf broke against the rocks. It was raining - a steady drizzle - as she climbed high into the cart, clutching her possessions in a rolled up apron, bumping through the lanes to Stratton.

She was to work for the Curate, Rev. Adams, and his wife Wilhelmina; to be their sewing maid and to work in the kitchen. They were good people, who lived as their religion demanded: kind to their servants and kind to the people of the town.

Emily Heard

The prayer ended, she sat back in the pew, and, as she did so she felt the child move in her body. As a fluttering butterfly, the feeling of life, of eternity.

She was tall and raw-boned with a fine sculpted face, her soft wavy hair drawn neatly behind her ears, blue eyes and a thin-lipped smile.

The Vicar's voice droned on and, seated in the shadow of one of the Church pillars, the watchmaker produced from his pocket a large gold watch and, having tapped the watch, proceeded to catch the Vicar's eye. They were all at Church that morning, the people of the town: Pickard the Registrar, Maynard the landlord of the New Inn, Yeo the boot maker, the blacksmith, the

5

wheelwright, the Tanners from the Tannery, grocer, butcher, baker and candlestick maker. Arrayed in their Sunday best, neat black worsted suits, large black hats. The women wore their finest bonnets and shawls, some of the farm labourers and their wives wore clogs, cleaned specially for churchgoing. The townswomen, seated across the aisle whispered and pointed in Emily's direction.

'The Curate's servant, and with child!'

'The disgrace! The scandal! The upcountry foreigner!'

She was tired, though it was but mid-morning. She had risen with the dawn as the first light filtered through the trees, to clean the huge black monster of a stove that roared all day to be fed with wood and coal, to blaze and flame so Cook could work to prepare the many meals for the curate's household.

Emily Heard at New Buildings, Marhamchurch

Cook was kind to her and, although no words were spoken, she knew that Cook was aware of her despair and condition, and remembered the rosy-cheeked miller's son who delivered the flour and whose pale-blue eyes lit up at the sight of Emily, with her hand-span waist and soft wavy brown hair. She remembered flirting with John and, though not as tall as her, he possessed a strength that drew her to him.

She remembered the Summer - that Summer. It was a gloriously hot, once-in-a-lifetime Summer. The leaves on the trees turned gold long before the Autumn came and the earth became parched and bare. In the fields the corn ripened early, the golden barley waving in the summer wind making waves as a sea; a sea of golden ripening corn. She remembered how hand in hand they ran through the barley laughing together like children, while the sun blazed in an Italian blue sky and the wind whispered in the corn. They chose their favourite place in the corner of the field, shadow from the hedge cooling their hideaway.

Lying naked in the corn, the sun pouring down on her eager body, she felt the warmth of the sun on her bare breasts and the wind blowing a caress across her nakedness. But that was as a dream now - and long ago. The Vicar intoned the final prayer and the congregation dispersed, each going their separate way.

The next morning, the town slept in the sun: a cat asleep in a doorway, horse and cart labouring up the hill through the narrow street, the only sound the constant tap, tap of the hammer at the wheelwrights and down at the bottom of the hill the ring of the blacksmith's anvil. On the corner between the two main streets stood a Milliners and Drapers. The cobbled way outside the shop was caked in mud and the owner of the shop cleaned energetically among the stones. A man driving a pony and trap travelling down the hill paused and whispered, "Ers comin', 'Ers comin'.' The shopkeeper listened intently and, borne on the summer air, he heard the rustle of taffeta, the swish of a skirt and the quick light walk of a woman. He shouted to the children playing with their hoops in the street, 'Go inside, go inside'. A tiny woman pushing a perambulator with iron clad wheels increased her pace up the hill and entered a thatched cottage, closing the divided door behind her. Nothing stirred as the whisper of the skirt grew louder - the town was silent and deserted. The feather boa around her shoulders fluttered in the breeze as she strode with arrogant steps down through the town - the Squire's sister on her daily walk and inspection of the town. The townsfolk knew that if they were found to be on the street as she passed, they would be expected to doff their caps or curtsy to this elegant lady.

Life at the Mill was a constant struggle against the elements; to keep the mill-wheel turning - the sound of it turning as the sound of life itself - to keep the leat running Summer and Winter, to turn the wheel to grind the corn, on this their very existence depended. John's mother, the miller's widow, was a tiny frail shawl-covered figure but one who ran the Mill and Farm and ruled her children with a rod of iron. It was Sam who brought the message to the Mill. It was Sam who broke the news. The parlour maid at Miss King's house had delivered an important message, as Sam brought the sack of flour to the kitchen that morning. Miss King, the Squire's sister, had sent a message to the Miller's widow saying that she wished to see her on a matter of some importance and she would be calling at the Mill at three o'clock that afternoon. 'But why?', wondered Elizabeth, 'what was so important as to warrant a visit from one so grand?'

The day was spent cleaning the kitchens at the Mill, Polly and Lib exhausted by their efforts but the two sisters eager to please their mother. The higher kitchen was prepared for their special visitor: a fire lit in the grate, the leather sofa drawn closer to the fire and the slate floor scrubbed. The boys were ordered by their mother to sweep the lane and clean the mud from the yard. They heard the sound of ponies' hooves and the creak of wheels and at three o'clock the trap driven by a groom with Miss King seated bolt upright drove into the Mill yard.

'Good afternoon', she said stiffly, her eyes surveying the widow woman and her two daughters dressed in their black dresses and neat white aprons.

'Good afternoon Madam,' Elizabeth replied, 'will you please come in.'

Helped by the groom, the lady alighted from the trap. She stooped low, as the doorway was low and narrow and she gathered her skirt around her as she entered the tiny room.

Elizabeth felt a sense of foreboding as she bade her visitor to be seated on the leather sofa. Miss King stated her case - speaking slowly and very softly - she said, 'There are rumours in the town that your son John has been keeping company with the Curate's new maid, Emily. It is said,' (she paused dramatically) 'that she is with child'.

There was a silence in the room. Far away came the sound of the mill wheel and, somewhere, a dog barked.

'My son and Emily. Yes.' Elizabeth replied. 'That is right.'

'Do you understand, my good woman, the scandal that is causing in the town?'

'Really,' she thought, 'the ignorance of these peasant people.'

Miss King continued, 'She has drawn the attention of many men since arriving here from God knows where. I can have it arranged that she is sent packing and the child put into the Institution. I came here this afternoon to give you my help and advice - something I am sure you will accept. Have you lost your tongue, woman. It is your son I am trying to save.'

'And the child is my grandchild,' replied Elizabeth.

There was a silence in the room. The only sound the crackle and hiss of the logs on the fire. Elizabeth stood up - she was short, but as the lady was seated she dominated her - and she drew herself up to her full height. 'Madam', she said, speaking slowly and deliberately, 'the child you speak of is my grandchild - its father, my son - he will face his responsibilities, he will marry Emily Willoughby and the child will have a name. A name that is part of Stratton Town and, hopefully, will be for generations. I bid you good day Madam and ask you to leave my house.'

They were married in August 1896, were John and Emily: they travelled home to Swindon and her people; when they returned, they rented a tiny cottage at New Buildings, Marhamchurch; John walking through the lanes to the Mill each day. Times were hard and money very scarce.

It was November and bitterly cold, with fogs and frosts and occasional snow. At dawn, her waters broke. From the dawn to the late afternoon the back-breaking spasms continued. From screams of pain to a whimper, her voice was heard piercing the tiny cottage. The old woman from next door, who knew everything about women and childbirth, swore she'd seen nothing like it. As she pondered, beads of perspiration appeared on her brow. She suggested sending for the doctor, but there was no money in the house, no money at the Mill, no money for a doctor. The news spread among the family that John's Emily was dying, here on the narrow iron bed in the corner of the bare room.

Minnie was married to John's brother Tom. Minnie met Tom when he was learning his trade as a Tailor in Plymouth. She was very dainty and wore her clothes with a style and grace. She inherited a private income and lived her life in her own way. She was strict with her children - educated them all and walked to the Chapel in the valley each Sunday carrying a red parasol. She had received a smattering of education herself and the townspeople - some unable to read or write - came to her with their problems and woes. It was late in the November afternoon and the dusk was creeping in from the sea as Minnie, donning her hat and gloves, strode along the lanes from Stratton to Marhamchurch. As she neared the tiny cottage, the lamp in the window made a path of light to the doorway. A cat brushed against her skirt as she entered the tiny kitchen. She sensed how silent the cottage seemed - an uncanny silence.

'Up here, Min.' John's voice called from above. 'Thank God you've come!'

She climbed the stair, lifted the latch of the door and could just distinguish in the gloom the shape of a woman covered by a grey blanket on the bed.

'Dear God!' she cried. 'She's dying. We must have the doctor or she will surely die! And what of the child?'

At her words, John burst into tears. 'There's no money, Min' he sobbed, 'we have no money - not a florin between us!'

'Something must be done', Min replied. 'I have the money. I will pay!

Will, next door owns a horse. Send him to Stratton at once for the doctor. I will pay!'

As the stars appeared and the frost turned the fields a winter white on that November evening, the Doctor arrived. Within the hour, the triumphant cry of a baby echoed through the cottage. A baby boy was born to Emily and that night, November 6th 1896, my father, John Heard, was born.

Emily and John Heard at New Buildings, Marhamchurch

The Mill in the Valley

Voices in mill meadow on a summer afternoon, children's laughter bringing memories of long ago when voices and laughter blended with the sounds of the life of the mill.

The farm carts rumbling through the narrow lanes, the shouts of the men, the music of the water as it splashed and fell over the mill wheel, the cooing of the pigeons, all a part of the life of the mill in the valley. The River Strat flows through the ancient town of Stratton; for many years its course was divided by a weir and a sluice gate, the main river continued to flow, winding its way through the wooded valley, the other becoming the mill leat, its course decided and the power used to drive the massive granite stones to grind the corn at the mill. There was a constant battle to keep the mill wheel turning, fighting drought in the Summer and ice in Winter, the wheel so entwined with their lives, a disaster indeed if the power of the water was lost and the wheel ceased to function.

At the height of the summer, on a picked midsummer day, a gang of a dozen men would arrive, armed with picks and shovels to clean out the leat. The water was turned off at Stratton then the water wheel was started to grind corn and so drain the leat. The men dressed in their oldest clothes then shovelled the mud from the leat onto the banks, having cut the hedges. 'Drinkings' consisted of beef and potato pasty, apple pasty, carried in huge butter baskets and, at tea-time, splits and cake, steaming kettles of tea, carried out to the men in the fields by the women and, finally, at the end of the busy summer day, a hot meal served around the wooden table in the kitchen. The farmers from Stratton and district brought their corn to the mill, and paid the miller for the service of grinding. A bag of wheat would be returned to its owner, the meal on the top of the sack, then the bran and at the bottom of the sack the precious flour.

The mill was a two-storied building and the corn was weighed and pulled up through a hatch to the second floor, from where it was poured onto the massive stones; stones which were 'dressed' by the miller with a craftsman's skill, the 'dressing' consisting of cutting grooves from the granite stone.

The dredge corn (barley and oats) was emptied onto the stone without being sifted, but the wheat to be ground into soft snow-white flour was carefully sifted first. The 'seconds' (leftover grain) became the bread baked for the miller's children.

The dwelling house was separate from the mill, built onto the slope at the edge of a grassy platt, its position sheltered from the westerly wind. By the back door stood the pump, which creaked and clanked as its ancient arm was pulled and just beyond the back kitchen was the dairy, with its cool slate floor and table, keeping the butter and cream fresh for the market. In a far corner, beyond the neatly placed pasties and saffron cakes, stood the granite trough containing a 'salted pig'. On pig killing day a Mr Leach came to kill the pig; it was then laid down and scraped, using boiling water and the women were kept busy carrying buckets of water heated on the open chimney fire. The belly was cleaned to make hog's puddings; the women went down to the mill, up the steps and cleaned them while the water wheel was working. The staircase in the centre of the house consisted of narrow crooked stairs and, at the head of the stairs, there was a small landing leading to the bedrooms, their doors opened by latches. The rooms had low beamed ceilings and sloping floors. The smallest room built into the roof was used as an apple room, the precious gift of autumn; the rosy apples stored as so much treasure on the sloping floor.

There was a Lower Kitchen and a Higher Kitchen, and the Lower Kitchen was the hub of the activity at the mill, a low beamed room with an open fireplace, cloam oven, a long trestle table and wooden forms. The Higher Kitchen was used on special occasions, such as weddings and funerals and here, on quiet Sunday evenings, while the miller was away from home preaching at some tiny chapel, the family headed by the miller's wife would gather around the table and, by flickering candlelight, using the Bible (the only book in the house) the children at the Mill in the Valley were taught to read.

Jack, John and Fred Heard at Howard Mill

At Christmas it was in the Higher Kitchen that traditional family games were played. At this time a harmonium was transported by horse and cart, bumping its way from Stratton, so to enhance the singing of the Stratton carols and the music of the concertina echoed across Howard Valley.

11

The miller's nine children returned with their wives and children to pay homage to their tiny frail mother, to whom they owed much. Widowed by the typhoid epidemic at Stratton in March 1880, she carried the burden of running the mill and farming the land and she ruled her brood with a rod of iron.

The horses used at Howard Mill to pull the farm carts were fine animals, easy to handle and hard-working. Fred Heard and his uncles worked the mill and the flour business. His favourite mare was Rose. There was an affinity between them. Rose with her white blaze and Fred with his flour-covered clothes were a familiar sight around Stratton town. Then came 1914 and men and horses went to war - the horses to pull the guns in the battlefields of France. And so horses were shipped across the English Channel to depots along the Western Front.

However, Fred did see Rose again. The young soldier was mud spattered and exhausted and was marching in a column somewhere in France and as the column passed a line of tethered horses, a mare with a white blaze lifted her head and neighed. The solider broke ranks and fell on her neck, reunited, if only for a few moments in time with his favourite mare. Fred Heard returned safely from France and continued as the miller at Howard Mill Stratton until the late 1950's, when the business of grinding corn for flour ceased. The wheel was removed from the mill wall and so the mill at the Mill in the Valley stopped forever.

Howard Valley from Headon's Park Wall.

The Cottage

I knocked upon the window,
Come in my Granny said
Wafting from the kitchen
The smell of baking bread.
The ring of the blacksmith's anvil
And children's voices in the playground
From the school across the way,
Bleating sheep driven over the bridge
To market on a hot summer's day.
The bubble in the window above my bed,
The disorientated view of the church on the hill,
The scent of the geraniums ablaze on the window sill,
The acrid smell of wood smoke
From the fire upon the hearth,
The fire was burning always
To keep the cob wall dry,
Memories of a tiny girl who fell fast asleep,
Snuggled deep deep in a feather Tye*

*Emily Heard at
Howls (Tudor)
Cottage
1913- 1958*

*Feather Mattress

LOT 7. All that COTTAGE and two GARDENS called
PART HOWLS

Situate at Howls Bridge in the Town of Stratton, abutting on the main road from Holsworthy to Bude, and now in the occupation of Mr. F. Hambly as a yearly Ladyday Ten·nt, determinable as aforesaid.

No. on Tithe Map.	Description.	Area A.	R.	P.
779, 780, 781	House, Garden, &c.	0	0	23

The Tithe is apportioned at 6d., the present value of which is 4½d.
The Land tax is assessed at 3/4½ and the rent is apportioned at £4/10.

As to Lots 6, 7 and 8 and part Lot 2. The Tenement called "Howls" or "Holles" is described in the Duchy of Cornwall Receipt mentioned in these Special Conditions as being part of that Duchy's Manor of Stratton Sanctuary. Each purchaser of these Lots will buy subject to whatever (if any) incidents of tenure or reservations may exist in favour of the said Duchy under any of the said Duchy of Cornwall Assessionable Manors. Acts or any other Acts or otherwise howsoever in right of the aforesaid or any other Manor or otherwise. The Vendors cannot and shall not be asked to define what may be parts of the said (or, any other) Manor. No requisition whatever either for compensation or otherwise shall be made herein.

Top: The purchase of Howls cottage and sold by Misses Bray of Langford, Marhamchurch.
Left: Sale of the estate by the Thynnes of Kilkhampton and noted by John Heard on Howard Mill billhead.

The Chimney Corner Tale

The farmhouse stands at the crossroads. Follow the winding lanes from the village - lanes narrowed by the encroaching wild flowers - and there at the crossroads dominating the landscape stands the farmhouse: a rambling building with many chimneys, its roof low to protect against the westerly winds, its stone walls mellowed by age, a farmstead and a home.

Here live the people who tend their sheep through the long winter nights, who milk the herd at dawn, who plough and reap and sow, their lives a constant battle with the elements. Here live the people who are part of the soil of their land - these precious acres part of their very souls - born here and following a way of life soon to pass into history. These people are wise, an inborn wisdom fighting the wind and rain and snow makes wheeling and dealing with people an easy matter. Insular, with their own ways and customs; Church, Chapel, the Young Farmers' Club, the WI, fat stock shows and markets, couples encouraged to wed to boost the family fortunes - a few more acres for the next generation.

Across the yard, by the back door, a dog, a collie dog, slept peacefully on a sack until the time came to obey his master's whistle and go to work 'rounding up' the sheep and cattle.

Through the back door, and into the back hall, where slate flagged floor was scrubbed every day, its colour changing with the passing of the hour. A staircase led from the hall to an open gallery, giving the hall space and light. The first room inside the hallway was the dairy. The coolest room in the house - cool even on a hot summer day - also slate floored, it housed the separator to change the milk to cream and the butter churn to produce delicious creamy butter. In the centre of the dairy and filling the rest of the room stood a slate table. Here the farmer's wife set out her pasties, and eggs were placed in neat rows.

The front door of the farmhouse was never opened except for weddings and funerals. The front door was set with panels of coloured glass and a footpath bordered by two neat flower beds bordered by shells led up to it.

At Christmas, the 'best front room' was used; the fire lit in the hearth, the piano played and the old farmhouse brought to life. The room was filled with generations of farming families, rosy cheeked, cloth-capped; the hunting, shooting, fishing, yeoman stock gathered here to eat, drink and celebrate another year.

The kitchen was the centre of the household, the hub of activity. Here crickets chirped behind the stove, and the long wooden table with trestles each side was set for the many meals of the day. The master seated at the head, the workmen at the far end of the table, as suited their status in the life of the farm. As evening came, the farmer's wife bustled along the hallway carrying a freshly trimmed oil lamp. The lamps were as a part of her, striding from room to room, leaving her shadow on the beamed ceiling.

By the side of the barn was the duck pond. They were wayward, the farm ducks, and the nightly ritual of shutting them in a shed against the wily fox became a part of life.

When the toil of the day was over the farmer, seated in the chimney corner on the side of the huge hearth, would throw another log on the fire, adjust the crook from which a kettle hung and, puffing his pipe contentedly, commence to tell the tales of long ago -

The cottage nestles in the valley between the grand Georgian house, with its marble portico high on the hill, and the road and river below. The girl who lived at the cottage watched the river as part of her way of life. The river ebbed and flowed and the tides flooded the estuary. The seagulls cry in the early morning, the men fishing by the bridge, their nets spread across the river, watching for the first salmon. The cherry trees in Spring, the cobble quay, the little white town. The dappled patterns in the mud and water as the tide receded, a heron motionless on one leg and the timelessness of the sunset across the bay.

The young squire, having dined well and recollected the highlights of the day, was seated in his favourite chair by the fire. With the gathering dusk, the spirit of the sea called him - from beneath the ancient rocks came the call of the tide. Calling the dogs, he strode the wooded lane to the sea.

Always at this time, the sea called and he would answer, wherever he was on his estate, often many miles inland. Like all Cornish people he could sense in the air the turn of the tide, feel the salt spray, a lift of spirit as the tide turned, as life turned. As he watched the rhythm of the waves beating on the rocks he remembered the girl with the long black hair and sparkling blue eyes, remembered their time together, their love and happiness. Marriage was impossible, she was but a servant, but he would remain a bachelor for the rest of his days and would watch over her and his son.

The windows of the inn were ablaze with light, the early evening twilight had started to creep into the little room and the sound of raucous laughter invaded the night. The farmers were celebrating Market Day; the one day of the week when they left the empty spaces of the fields and the backbreaking routine of their lives to relax, to enjoy and to live a little. The farmers stood obediently, caps in hand, in the flag-stoned corridor to wait their turn to pay their rent to the Squire's Bailiff seated by the open window. They had finished the business of the market, seen their cattle sold as the auctioneer's voice echoed across the pens, standing in the drizzling rain smelling the animal smell of the sheep and hearing the belving of the cattle.

There was a buzz of gossip this day, a whisper passed from one to another as they drove through the narrow lanes to the Market and Inn. Why? For what reason should he receive the tenancy of such a profitable farm? One or two of the farmers, red-faced and slightly tipsy, nodded and winked. They remembered the girl at the cottage by the river, the stories of how the young Squire visited, his horse tethered by the fence, the child born at the cottage; the Child with no name, but stamped with the clear-cut features of the aristocrats.

Across the front hall at the farmhouse was the most intriguing room in the house, Granny's room - her domain. Orders had come from the Manor at the time her son moved into the farm that she was to receive a cooked meal, her own room and a lifetime of being cared for by however many generations until her death. Here, from this tiny room she dominated the life of the farm.

The ormolu clock takes pride of place, on the granite fireplace in the converted barn. It was the centrepiece of their lives, this farming clan. The clock, given by the Squire to his love all those years ago and moved many times from the opulence of the Manor to the cottage by the river and to the farmhouse and finally, to the splendour of the converted barn.

The farmer told the legend of his ancestors while seated in the Chimney Corner all those long, long years ago.

They still have an aura and mystery about them, the folks at the farm at the crossroads. Aloof from the other farmers, their features stamped with aristocratic good looks, their clipped voices commanding attention. On Open Day, they still visit the Manor on the hill and wander the red-carpeted hallways viewing the portraits; study the portraits and then smiling secretly at each other they remember the Chimney Corner Tale, told as the fire burned brightly in the hearth and the east wind blew its gales against the Farmhouse at the Crossroads.

The Horse Dealers

The evening sunlight glinted through the dark fir trees and cast its spell of light and shadow on the brick walls of the cottage. The hand of Autumn had caressed the woods around and the magnificent beeches were burnished with copper and gold. A pall of smoke wafted its way from the chimney through the trees to the sky beyond. An upstairs was open and a muslin curtain fluttered in the evening breeze.

At the end of the orchard a white gate stood open to the road that wound its way to the village beyond. In a field nearby, three piebald ponies munched contentedly at the grass, at times lifting their heads to sniff the wind.

Around a small cobbled yard, the stable doors creaked gently in the wind. The kitchen was small and, on a black-leaded stove, a kettle sang. The windows were glassed with tiny panes and as evening came the room grew darker.

The *man* dozed in his favourite chair by the stove, his feet on the stool by the table. He dozed, but there was an alertness about him, a watchfulness, a tension.

Then, borne on the still autumn air, came the sound of trotting hooves, the shout of a drover, and a string of ponies jostled and trotted along the dusty road to the open orchard gate.

Rickson, the drover, was very tall and thin. He walked with a long stride, clad in a long grey coat and battered trilby hat. At times, as he drove the horses from faraway markets and fairs, he would sleep in farmers' barns and turn the horses into a grassy meadow; pooving* as the Romanies did. At the hour before the dawn, he would steal away with the horses, their bellies full of rich grass from an unsuspecting owner.

He was tired and thirsty for he had walked the ten miles from the Market Town where the Man had purchased the semi-wild ponies. It had been a long hot day, but soon he would sleep in the *man's* barn, having washed at the pump, quenched his thirst on a basin of tea and savoured a hunk of bread and cheese.

In the Winter when life was hard, he would sing in the streets and beg for money, wads of newspaper inside his coat to protect against the icy cold. But for today, the sun shone, the people were kind and life was good.

From the orchard came the sound of children's voices, and three small black-haired boys and a rosy-cheeked girl climbed the orchard gate to inspect the horses. The *man* called to the boys asking their opinion of his purchases and they shouted a reply, their voices echoing through the woods.

The children formed a circle around the well seated on the grass, as a supper of bread and cheese and a jug full of cider was brought from the cottage. The

18   *leaving horses to graze overnight in someone's field.

Bampton Fair where the horse dealers bought ponies

evening breeze played with the silk muffler around the *man*'s neck as he leaned against the tree, contentment on his face. It had been a good day and there was peace here; and quiet after the noise and bustle of the horse fair, with its shouting, pushing and bargaining.

He was a stocky man in his late forties, with sparkling blue eyes, a head of dark curly hair and a magnificent moustache streaked with grey. There was about him an air of animal magnetism: something in his walk, the set of his head and his bright blue eyes, which drew people to him - men and women alike. The women admired his charm and sex appeal; the men admired his good will and generosity; no one was turned from his door, there was always food and a bed - shelter and comfort.

He thought back on the events of the day, the crowd of dealers at the horse fair. He was successful as a dealer. Much of the cunning and knowledge of the horse trade came from his Romany wife and her father, Old Reuban. He remembered Old Reuban and the tales told of him; how owning the wildest fastest horse in the district, he whipped the animal as he rode through the village and the villagers would curse and draw their children closer; how with craft and skill (though unable to read or write) he had amassed a fortune wheeling and dealing, buying and selling. Forsaking the Romany life on the road, Reuban purchased an old rambling house, there raised his children and lived a gaujo life though the Romany ways and tongue remained with him still.

He had been dead these ten years since. On his death, his hard-earned sovereigns were tossed into a large black umbrella. His children, the three sisters and their men, with Maddie Lylla's child in a battered pram, set out on the road from inn to inn, from town to town, 'til all was lost in a wild drunken spree.

The sun went down beyond the trees and the autumn wind blew colder as they entered the cottage and, throwing more wood on the fire, drew together sitting close around its cheery blaze in the kitchen. The children were given the task of taking a basin of tea to Rickson in the barn and there they listened to his tales of the road.

The fire burned low in the grate and stirring himself, the *man* climbed the little stair to his bed. Tomorrow he would be away again buying more horses ready to sell at the Saturday Market. He set the alarm for five; he would catch the train at six. There would be new horses, new dealers and new women.

Maddie awoke to the song of the birds and the rays of the morning sun streaming through the window. She told the time by the strength of the sun and soon she must rise and drive the children to school in the pony and trap. The *man* was gone; it would be dark when he returned. The house was silent without him; he was its life and their lives revolved around him.

She must find something for the children to eat. There was more in the house when the *man* was home; without him they managed as best they were able. She hoped the Russian with his dancing bear wouldn't come today. She was afraid of the bear and gave them sixpence to be rid of them. It was all right when the *man* was home but, at times, she was afraid alone with the children at the cottage in the woods.

It was hard work to collect the sticks, chop the wood, draw water from the well, keep the stove going, cooking, cleaning and washing, caring for her charges, a task for one so young. But she was strong, with an inner courage coming from her Romany ancestors. She was plump, rosy-cheeked, had sparkling brown eyes, a mass of dark auburn hair tumbling on her shoulders, a ready wit and a warm smile.

She knew how to handle the *man* and if she needed new shoes or a dress, she knew how to wile the money from him. The first time, when she was but fifteen, he gave her a beautiful gold pendant that she treasured above all else.

There were good times, living with the *man* as his woman and there were bad times, when money was scarce, bills were owed, cheques bounced; as risky as a card game, this world of horse dealing.

She opened the window and gazed across the yard to the meadow beyond. The horses grazed peacefully, their manes gleaming in the sun. They were contented and gentle now, but she recalled, with horror, one morning in a town nearby.

It was mid-day in the city: the aroma of freshly made coffee drifted from café doors, the newsboys shouted, 'Mid-day, Mid-day'. The city toffs alighted with their ladies from cabs and, somewhere, a barrel organ played. As she walked along, she felt the stones of the pavement through the thin soles of her shoes. Dodging in and out of the crowd, she saw him. There - in the centre of the city traffic with tram, cars and buses around - she saw the boy clinging grimly to a string of bucking, prancing horses. To the others in the milling crowd he was just a lad, a gypsy boy caught in the hell of the city traffic, but to her he was 'dear blood' - part of her very being. She stood horrified as he fought to hold the lead horse as it reared up in front of the thundering tram. Years after, she would recall the horror of those moments. The tram driver shouted and cursed as the horses plunged and reared. Eventually, a policeman arrived, helped the boy hold the horses and they dragged them away, still prancing and kicking, down the street to the market.

She drove the three children through the lanes to the village school, a low-roofed building surrounded by a stone wall. She had been eager to learn and absorbed all knowledge but, because of her life and her people, she felt a resentment from the teacher and so, when the time had come to leave, she had done so with a sense of relief.

Waving goodbye to the children, she collected the bread from the village Bakery; no money changed hands because a horse was exchanged for bread at the beginning of the year. It was warm in the morning sun and she wandered along the Village Street until she came to the Church hidden among the trees. It was a weekday morning; the Church would be empty for her alone. The church door creaked as she pushed it open, the iron handle cold in her hand. She listened before she entered its stillness but no sound broke the calm autumn morning. The Church was dark and silent; her footsteps echoed across the slate floor, a beam of sunlight lighting her path. Nothing disturbed its stillness, only the silence filled with the ghosts of chanting priests of long ago and the singing of long-dead villagers. She knelt in the pew to pray. From inside the Vestry came the sound of women's voices. Like a shadow she fled: like the flicker of a candle, as a startled deer she was gone, closing the wooden door behind her. Back to the hills, back to the moor and the heather, the girl from nowhere, the gypsy girl looking for her God. She ran to where the horse was tethered by the village shop and, climbing into the trap, she called to the horse and set off at a brisk trot to the cottage among the trees.

Charlie was short, with a mass of grey hair and a white beard. He had worked for the *man* for six years: he dug the garden, cleaned out the stables, cleaned the tack and was general handyman about the place. He puffed his pipe and, setting his cap at a different angle, wiped his face with a grubby hand. He could hear Maddie singing in the kitchen preparing the meal for the *MAN* and the dealers, and then he would receive his half-sovereign wage. He heard the sound of voices, the traps pull up and the shouting and laughing as the *man* and his dealer friends neared the cottage.

There were three of them: Spalding with his smart city clothes, a Tattersalls bookie, an air of prosperity about him and a way with the women; Hyde was tall and thin, most of his dealing was done with the London costers, the horses and ponies sold by him went to pull their carts; Ernie Payne was considered a 'let-down', he didn't fit in with the others in his shiny bowler and shabby overcoat.

'My! My! What have we here?' asked Spalding, striding across the grass to the old man. 'I believe 'tis the village goblin!'. The others laughed and the old man stared at them, fear in his eyes. 'What shall we do with him? Let's give him a treat! Pull up the bucket, we'll put him down the well! Charlie looked for help, terrified they might carry out their threat, but the *man* was busy unharnessing the traps. 'Come on fellows - down the well with him!' He strode towards the old man. 'Perhaps not! Look Charlie, I've something to show you, look!' He pulled from his pocket a handful of bright new sovereigns, more than the old man had seen in a lifetime. 'See how they shine - See how they shine!' The sovereigns glowed in his hand, as so-much golden treasure.

Meanwhile, attracted by the voices and laughter, Maddie ran across the grass to the group beneath the trees. 'Let me see!' she cried. 'What a lot of money!' She focussed her beautiful brown eyes on Spalding and, giving him a flirtatious smile, she drew closer to him. Then, still laughing and flirting, she knocked the sovereigns from his hand and they scattered over the grass. Spalding swore and demanded that Maddie, Charlie and the other dealers search among the grass for the precious coins. Later that evening, as the last of the dealers' traps drew away and was lost to sight along the lane, Maddie called the old man to her. 'There you are Charlie - two sovereigns for you and two for me'. She looked at him in the gathering dusk and, smiling secretly to herself, whispered 'and the gypsies will laugh at you!'

The flickering glow of the lamps on the trap was the only light as Maddie drove the *man* along the country lane. The pony was young and frisky and Maddie's arms ached as she fought to keep control. The darkness had fallen early, it was cold in the trap and the chill night air pierced her thin clothes. They were driving to Aldermaston to collect a wagon of horses.

She guided the pony into the Station Yard and, with the *man*, crossed the bridge to the platform beyond. The *man* gave her a penny. She bought a bar of chocolate from the red slot machine and munched it hungrily. The light of the full moon shone on the rails, making a silver pathway in the darkness. The *man* pulled a large silver watch from his pocket and, after a glance at the time, continued to gaze along he rail to the darkness beyond. Then, far away, they hear the rumble of wheels and, with a cloud of hissing steam, the train pulled into the platform. They ran to the end of the platform as the train braked. They heard the sound of hooves against wood and the high-pitched scream of a horse. Pulling open the wagon door, they discovered the horses packed inside. The *man* shouted to the guard to help him and, untying them one by one led them out onto the platform.

Maddie stood back because she could see there in the darkness, under the flaying hooves, lay a horse on the floor of the wagon; the others in their panic had trampled and stamped on the poor creature until death brought relief. Another for the knacker's Yard, another animal dead. There were many, and much suffering. Often, at dead of night, Maddie would creep to the stable and unlatch the heavy door to give them their freedom.

They tied the horses together and, with the *man* leading and Maddie driving the trap, set off for the cottage. It was the hour before the dawn, the darkest hour, the time when her ancestors moved on - always searching - never finding the perfect AtchinTan. As they led the ponies back through the lanes to the cottage, a new dawn broke; a thin pink line in a lightening sky.

* Stopping place

My Secret

Did they bury him on Bodmin Moor

Secretly at dead of night?

Did they bury him amid the gorse

In the path of the curlew's flight?

Did they lay him where the west wind blows

Bearing the mist from the sea?

Did they mark the place

'Neath the granite tor

Where ponies graze wild and free?

Will he find his place content at last

Under the blue Cornish sky

For they said he belonged with the gipsies,

That wild gaujo*Rye!

* *Gentleman*

To the South West

I will take the old roads
When I'm travelling home.
I will take the old ways,
The ways in childhood known.
I will travel the old lanes,
Where wandering cattle stray,
Glimpsing through the autumn leaves,
The curve of a well-loved bay.

I will dream of villages
And pub-bar crackling fires,
The sound of Sunday's calling bells
From granite spires.

To feel again in my Cornish blood,
The call of a turning tide,
To hear, borne on the breeze
On a summer night,
A choir on the harbour-side.
Mist on my face 'cross
Bodmin Moor,
The wind from the tor in my hair,

My spirit is free,
Returning to thee,
My Cornwall - once more!

Now the Visitors Have Gone

The visitors have gone, and Bude's beaches and town belong to it's residents once more. The beaches no longer echo to so many different dialects and accents: the beautiful people with their sun-tanned bodies and their surfboards no longer scan the ocean for the largest wave among the breakers. The beach cafés have finally sold out of ice cream and put up their shutters and only the breeze makes ripples on the surface of the swimming pool. Belle Vue is no longer a solid queue of cars, and the pedestrian crossing bleeps only occasionally. The amusement centres are quiet, and the shop tills no longer make music, whilst the hotels settle down to take local bookings for Christmas parties.

Bude Fair

In the years past, at this time, came Bude Fair with Anderton and Rowlands' great engines on the Wharf, the lights of the fair reflecting in the canal, and the sound of fairground music carrying across the sand hills to Nanny Moore's Bridge and echoing across the town.

Another year of Bude's life gone and melancholy Autumn heralding Winter. he Winter, when winds whip the Atlantic into a foaming cauldron, and the ocean itself laps the stone wall along the Strand, when the older men of Bude gather at the 'Carriers' and talk of those well remembered days of long ago. They remember gathering by the lock gates on a summer evening to see the 'Traly' come in on the tide; they remember swimming out to meet her, and to be greeted by a crew with real Cornish voices, men who spoke the language of the sea.

They remember the opening of the new swimming pool sixty years ago, which was built with great pride by a local builder and his men and opened, with great dignity, by the wife of the local squire; the Bude Town Band in those far off days, and the strains of the Furry Dance sounding down through the town, ending with a flourish outside the Falcon Hotel, where elegant ladies together with their

The Traly 1938

escorts, all resplendent in evening dress, assembled and applauded from the steps of the Hotel; a Harry Roy Band playing at the Grenville Hotel, that centre of Bude's social scene in the 1930's where local functions were celebrated in style.

The remember too the Southern Railway Station and the air of expectancy as the platform bell heralded the imminent arrival of the 'Atlantic Coast Express', and the hollow sound of tramping feet across the wooden floor of the booking hall as the visitors arrived - all the way from London - to make their way to the waiting taxis and the 'Falcon' horse bus to convey them in style to their final destinations in and around the town.

These older men at the 'Carriers' remember when in wartime days, Lord Haw-Haw, the Nazi propagandist, caused quite a sensation when he casually mentioned the swans gliding on Bude canal in one of his broadcasts; they remember the sound of the laundry hooter at one o'clock, and the two bells of St Michael's Church ringing out the quarters and the hours; they also remember the quacking of the ducks on river and canal and the smell of fresh-baked bread from the bakeries in Lansdowne Road and the Leven Bakery, and wafting over from far-off Flexbury Bakery too; the neat crocodile

Nanny Moore's Bridge

27

of Grammar School pupils marching briskly down from Grammar to Primary School for lunch, on their way often passing Mr Gist, the carrier's lorry waiting in the Strand to be loaded with much needed supplies, and cheerful residents all the way from the village on the hill, Kilkhampton.

In the cold dawn of a Sunday morning, the still-burning Headland light brought memories of the Saturday night before, when many of the young people of Bude met their destiny and many a heart was broken after the Ball - the Ball at the Headland Pavilion, Bude.

Many well remembered sights and sounds are gone, but Bude's seascapes remain the same and, as the sun goes down, Lundy Light still blinks across Bude Bay, but ....

> To be born near the roar of the sea,
> To live in the sound of the sea,
> Is a part of life itself,
> With the high tides of life - and the low -
> Here, in dear old 'Boode'.

Ships at Bude

Pathfields

To walk across the fields once more -
To follow the treasured way from village to shore,
Caress the granite millstone embedded in the grassy knoll
And take the path towards the seas
Where Atlantic breakers roll.
See an ocean liner passing by
Reflective white on a clear blue sky,
Children in brightly coloured clothes
Flitting by like butterflies.
Take this path to school on a summer morn
And hear the wind in the standing corn,
The shout of the crowd at football games
Played by generations of lads with local names.
The call for the cows at milking time,
The setting sun, with light sublime,
The frolicking lambs, the kissing gates,
Shady glade, and running stream.
There are seats for the old to sit and dream
For all things must pass.

Pathfields, there are seat where the old can sit and dream!

A Sunday School Anniversary

The sound of the harmonium through the open chapel door blended with the song of the birds rejoicing in praise on the hot May morning. The farmers, local businessmen, and farm workers had gathered to celebrate the Sunday School anniversary once more. Generations had gathered here in the little chapel; generations from the same farms and hamlets. Christenings, marriage and death had been celebrated between its tiny walls. The sunlight filtered through the windows and poured its golden light on to the bunches of primroses freshly picked by the pupils of the Sunday School, and pinned with great precision to the platform curtain. The organist played a little louder; the music reached crescendo and with a scuffling of feet and murmur of voices, the choir and Sunday School took their places on the platform. It was deemed a great privilege to sit on the platform and to be asked to sing for the Anniversary. The preacher took his place in the pulpit and the service began. Hymns and tunes - anniversary specials - practised for weeks beforehand. A matter of honour between each village chapel and, horror of horrors if two chapels inadvertently chose the same swinging tunes! The service continued with an occasional solo, or recitation from one of the tiny tots centred front stage. A golden-haired one would be coaxed to its feet, urged on by a Sunday School teacher seated in the front pew. Numerous parents, aunts and uncles would offer advice until the small child, after gabbling something quite incoherent, would resume its seat, amidst a storm of applause.

The preacher, usually a local farmer, would begin his sermon, followed by a story for the children. The congregation dozed gently as his voice droned on and, having cast a discerning eye at the various fashions present, and wondering what would be waiting for lunch in the old farm kitchen at the end of the winding farm lane, made the important decisions of the week ahead. The final hymn being sung, in which the congregation joined in with gusto, the doors would be opened and aunts in veiled hats, uncles in new navy suits, boys in new leather shoes and first long trousers and girls in best straw hats, frocks and neat cotton socks would walk sedately out into the morning sunlight. Outside the chapel another ritual took place: having shaken hands with the preacher, small groups formed of relatives and friends to discuss various country topics. The men unanimously took the conversation to the weather, state of the crops, price of land and cattle and whether the sermon was too long. The women discussed Mrs Somebody's hat, whether her skirt was too short and who was expecting a baby. The young people, having flirted outrageously in the chapel, pondered the question of who would be taking whom home from chapel in the evening. It was considered very important, this social gathering outside chapel and, unless someone was in disgrace, it was an accepted part of the ritual of a Sunday morning.

Anniversaries were more important because family gatherings were held, and relatives who rarely saw each other were expected to attend.

The procession of cars wended its way through narrow country lanes, sun dappled and bedecked with campion and bluebell to the entrance to the farm. The farm dogs barked noisily and scampered down the lane to greet the cars as they reached the iron bridge which spanned a river alive with trout, over the cattle grid and, with a clanging and changing into a low gear, climbed the hill up the lane with its many pits and ruts to the house which lay sleeping in the sun, its ancient chimney wafting smoke in the summer breeze. The front door was never opened except for weddings and funerals, so entrance was made through the back porch, with its array of wellingtons, overcoats, lamps trimmed and waiting to be lit and, occasionally, a plump rabbit hanging on a beam.

Titson Chapel

Just inside the back door stood the pump, its water crystal clear. Men came to wash here, the scent of the hayfield and the smell of the sun still on them as they laughed and splashed under its ancient arm, before sitting down to a supper after a hard day's toil in the fields. The kitchen was a low beamed long room with a settle in one corner, casting its shadow across the slate flagged floor. From the open fireplace came an acrid smell of burning wood, and from its centre hung the old iron crook. At the side of the fireplace was the cloam oven, from which delicious pasties to feed many generations were baked and taken to the harvest fields. Across one wall stood the dresser with china dogs and figurines and, by the window, stood the wooden table and on either side there were wooden benches. The family were seated at the table; the huge joint of beef was carved, grace was sung and twenty hungry appetites were satiated, appetites whipped up by the singing of hymns, the hot sun and the preacher's sermon. Sweet always consisted of huge bowls of junket made from milk straight from the cow, served with lashings of cream. A cup of tea and a home-made biscuit, and the meal was over.

The children laughed together and ran up the wooden back stairs, their feet making a clatter on the bare boards, changing out of their Sunday best and into play clothes. They knew that now, after the formality of the Sunday lunch they would have the long summer afternoon to play in the meadows and among the orchards where the bees buzzed in the hives and the apple blossom bloomed. They would visit the dark mysterious stable, where the magnificent shire horses were stabled. Huge shadows, munching in the darkness; the children were a little afraid of them, but remembered with pride the beautiful silver cup they had won for their master at the local ploughing championships. The shippens were long low buildings, built of grey stone; the bullocks were housed here and the walls were bedecked with rosettes won at the local fatstock show. Another tradition - the Fatstock Show. Tomorrow there would be the bustle and preparation for the anniversary tea. The ladies of the chapel had baked the splits, sponges and saffron cakes. Wafer thin bread and butter would be cut - a challenge as to who could cut the thinnest slices. Lots of thick, fruity home-made jam and crusty clotted cream, and the tea served piping hot by a lady invested with the honour of 'pouring tea'. The tea was served in the local Sunday School, a high lofty building, hot in Summer and draughty in Winter. Each sitting for tea was seated on long wooden forms arranged each side of a trestle table groaning with the weight of the food. Sugar was frowned on, a reflection from the days of John Wesley and his ban on sugar, a stand against the slave trade.

The heat and noise in the hall was overpowering and those waiting on neatly placed chairs to take their place at the table watched with thirsty throats as perspiring plump ladies with red faces hastily replenished the rapidly vanishing food. The older generation remembered other anniversaries when the party was larger. Before the uncles had emigrated to America where they worked for the Salvation Army in New York's Broadway. Before the one lost at Vimy Ridge. Before - before so many anniversaries ago.

When the evening came and the breeze blew across the valley and stirred the ripening corn, they would wander by the river bank and, watching a trout rise in a favourite pool, marking it for another day. The shadows would lengthen, an owl hoot and the last train for Bude rumble across the viaduct. Another time - another place - another Anniversary.

Cornish Voices

I hear familiar accents
As I passed by the narrow Cornish street,
I heard as from my childhood
The words and accents sweet.

I heard 'us' and 'er' and 'they' and 'them'
And 'How be you my dear!'
How wonderful to hear once more
Voices from yesteryear!

Did you know My Cornishman?

Did you know my Cornishman a-whistling in the sun?
Did you hear him praising God when the day was done?
Did you see his laughing eyes flirting with pretty girls?
Did you watch him cast a fly, there, where the river curls?
Did you watch him light his pipe, my Cornishman so tall?
Playing with the children, shadow rabbits on the wall.

Hands of the Miller's son,
The granite wheel of toil,
They took him 'cross the Tamar,
'Cross the bridge at old Greystone,
He died across the Tamar,
Never to come back,
My beloved Father, My Cornishman,
My Jack.

Shop on the Corner

The wooden till with the brass handle stands on the kitchen top at the house in the close. It is silent now. The till from the shop on the corner in Stratton, its bell silent, its wooden drawers are empty. Its handle well worn, its task well done. How many times it rang at the shop on the corner, how much its sound was the very centre of shop life.

John Heard and the errand boy.

My father John Heard founded his grocery business in 1919 renting the premises from Charlie Davies, the previous tenant Albert Jeffery having been killed in the 1914-18 war.

The business was an old-fashioned grocers. Orders were called for in the morning and delivered in the late afternoon by an errand boy on a bicycle. A succession of commercial travellers called during the course of the day, and goods were delivered to the shop by various lorries and vans. Some goods came by train and were delivered by local carrier. The shop sold yeast, stored in a soft cloth bag and flour, soft, white as snow fro the mill at Howard Mill.

Old Skills

Candles, night lights, Zebo to black lead grates, starch, blue bags and Sunlight soap for wash day. Sides of bacon and cloth wrapped cheese - a skill to bone a side of bacon and skin a cheese. Lard was delivered in blocks, cut into half pound squares and wrapped in grease proof paper to be sold. Currants and sultanas were delivered in large boxes, a square of purple paper place on the scale and then the mark of a grocer - the skill to make a spill-proof bag from the paper to contain the currants. My mother cooked large hams in a huge black pot on the kitchen range, cooked to perfection and sliced on the bacon machine. A machine cleaned and polished each night as the shop closed. During the winter, when my father was delivering orders in the late afternoon, as the gathering dusk fell, the lights of the shop attracted the tramps fro the workhouse on the hill, peeping through the windows, they made may mother uneasy and afraid and she was pleased when my father returned.

Buckingham's cows were driven through the streets at regular times each day and their creamy milk was the secret of delicious home made ice cream sold at the shop.

Heard's grocers, Bissats & Saunders shoe shops and Bay Tree hotel.

At eight in the morning, and during the lunch hour the shoe repairers from Saunders and Bissat's workshop congregated on the corner for a chat before returning to work. The noise of their machines, a part of the day.

The summer came, and with it the visitors driving from Exeter via Holsworthy, down the winding road, catching a first breathtaking view of the sea from Hobacott Down.

The pace of life quickened. The shop was packed with customers for several months and it became an amateur visitor's centre, supplying information and directions to numerous farm cottages. Issuing fishing licences for the River Board and information from my father, a keen angler, of the best trout pool in the district.

As a child at night in my bedroom above the shop, I would hear the sound of the local policeman trying the shop door to be sure all was safe in our little town.

During the war a constant stream of convoys of tanks, lorries and guns, American and British, trundled through Stratton and the shop on the corner gave welcome food and drink to the motorcycle outrider who arrived ahead to guide the convoys around the tricky dangerous corner. The size of the school numbers increased as evacuees from Plymouth and London were billeted around the town.

Cricket

Games of cricket were played on summer nights and Cockney voices blended with Cornish accents. We welcomed them and the church room was used for extra classrooms. A secret

Barbars shop and cottages

Snow at Stratton.

code was arranged, any child using the outside loos at the school would signal to the other children when a convoy was driving past, and at playtime we would climb the school railings and shout with excitement as the troops threw sweets, chewing gums and fruit from the lorries. The clocks were adjusted to double summer time and the daylight hours were wonderfully long. Early each morning trucks carrying Negro soldiers passed through on the way to Holsworthy. Whatever the weather, rain or snow, they were always in trucks open to the elements.

Rationing was a part of life. Ration books were stamped; points for canned foods were bundled and taken to the food office in Bude. Evenings were spent by the wireless listening to the cynical tones of Lord Haw Haw, Germany calling! Germany calling! And the horror when one night he spoke of the swans on Bude Canal and we thought the invasion was imminent. Several servicemen's wives were customers at the shop and would speak of air raids bombing over Germany from which their husbands may not return.

Great excitement at school when we received an invitation to the American's party. We were collected in army lorries and taken to Bude Picture House to see a film and then to the Headland for tea. The food consisted of things we had only dreamt about, because of the rationing, and the Americans were most generous and kind. Te pubs in Stratton were alive with music and laughter, the men enjoying their hours before embarking for war.

Cherished

The Lecture Hall (now the Community Hall) throbbing to the incessant beat of a dance band, packed with British and American troops, dancing to the songs of the day: Deep in the Heart of Texas, Silver Wings in the Moonlight, and the most poignant of all, If I Had my way Dear you'd never Grow Old. They will be remembered by us. Even through childlike eyes and thoughts at that time, remembered and cherished, those memories of the war and the shop on the corner in Stratton.

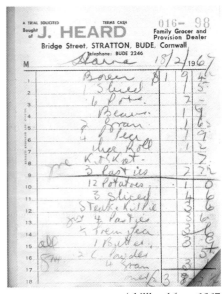

Stratton shops in the fifties.

A billhead from 1967

Heard's in the fifties

Bide-a-While

Joan and John Humphries on the
Clapper Bridge.

Bide-a-while on Stratton town's bridge,
Where a river of memories flow,
Picture the shadows of the past,
Reflected in ripples below.

Imagine the folk who crossed the bridge,
A part of their way of life,
Imagine the lovers meeting here,
For many the choice of a wife.

Children crossed on Clapper Bridge,
A safer way to school,
Children's laughter echoes still,
By the old mill pool.

Stand-a-while remembering,
Of the town that once we knew,
A lot of water has flowed under the bridge,
Since the market day lorries drove through.

Many far-away bridges are crossed,
And many beautiful bridges you will see,
But Stratton town bridge is the bridge of time,
For an old Strattonian like me.

Building the new bridge

Stratton Remembered

When dusk crept into the valley from the distant sea, and the lamps were lit in the cottages, the men who laboured in the fields all day strode through the village, across their shoulders the faggots of wood and the shovels and scythes of their trade. The farms were a part of the town, the cows brought in from the fields twice a day to be milked and clocks set by the time of their passing. Corn and hay were carried, horses and carts brought through the town, through narrow alleys. Corner Gardens, the scene of many a minor disaster, with horse and cart on one side and a load of hay wedged firmly on the other.

Unveiling the war memorial - 1914-18 war.

Stratton alive, Stratton busy.

Market day, Saturday, fortnightly. A stir of expectancy about ten o'clock as the first farmers arrive, calves belving in the trailer, then an occasional cattle lorry. The streets begin to fill with bustling people and, on a summer's day, the town is packed with visitors, the streets so filled with folk they find it difficult to walk on the pavement. People greeting each other, people who are part of each other, friends and relatives all meet at Stratton Market. A little more activity, a few more sheep driven by with much shouting and waving of sticks and, despite their obstinacy, over the bridge to the Market (now Parc Fer Close). A laugh, a wave, a farmer's joke - all a part of Stratton Market. With Peter Kivell's voice echoing across the cattle pens; will prices be high today?

Farmers from Stratton district, farms handed down from generation to generation: 'Thorne', the name mentioned in the Assize Rolls for Cornwall in 1302, 'Howard and Howard Mill' (Heyford 1284), 'Pollards' from the family name of Pollard (Blanchminster Grove 1389). Marsh, Moreton Pound, Oxen Park, Cann Orchard, Mapowders, Grove, Morton Leigh, Cross Lanes: Stratton farmers from Stratton farms at Stratton Market.

Market Day ....

The Kings Arms, its licence extended to accommodate the Market, the murmur of voices, the chink of glasses. The hub of activity, Harry and Olive Chesterton busy with their customers. Farmers with cheques to change, farms with shopping lists, the Stratton shops were a part of them - and those well-remembered Saturdays long ago. The last market was held at Stratton in December 1966.

Carnival

To spend a childhood in a Cornish town as beautiful as Stratton was a rich blessing indeed. The village was real then. People knew each other, belonged to each other, hated each other, helped each other. From generation to generation the same family lived in the same house or cottage, there was a pattern and a rhythm to life. To watch the seasons change, to know the characters of the town.

Mrs Ward's Aunt Jeff times her life without the discipline of a clock, arising

Methodist lunch at Lecture now Community Hall, 1936

Sports Day. Left to right: Reg Kelly, Leighton Saunders, Jack Heard, John Wickett, Tom & Bettine Ward, Charles Kivell, Rev. Williams. Front right: Raymond Cann.

from her bed with the sun and closing her day with the last of its rays. Miss White, the Alderman's daughter from London, feeding her cats during the war on best steak. Mrs Oke, who ran a second-hand shop: 'You are my sunshine', her one and only vocal offering. The peddler, who came with his horse and cart selling pots and pans around the town. Yeo, the Town Crier, informing Stratton folk of the events at *Bude*.

The errand boys whistling as they made their deliveries on shop bicycles. The gang meeting on the corner, seated on the window sill to discuss girl friends, secrets and the power of a motorbike. The Policeman, patrolling the streets at night trying the shop doors. Doctor King, driving by in his coupe, studying the village children brought into the world by the kindly gentleman.

During the War, to play cricket down the Leat on a warm summer's night with the evacuees; Cockney voices blending in with the native Cornish. The Lecture Hall (now Community Hall) throbbing to the incessant beat of a dance band, packed with young American and British troops, who were welcome strangers for a time. But then the town returned to its steady pace of life once more.

Stratton boasted its own Band, the Drama Group - The Stratton Strollers, the Trade Association, the Police Station.

A child was born, an old person died - the town's people attending the funeral and blinds drawn and shops closed as a token of respect as the cortege passed by.

The Trade Association in the Stratton Carnival

Presentation of mugs - Coronation Day May 13th 1937 by Dr King in the school yard.

My View of Stratton

It means nothing to the newcomer - My View

They have no memories or history,

The history of my view.

The slated roof of schoolhouse,

Where once as child I played,

The farm upon the hill top,

Where wandering cattle strayed.

They don't remember harvest time,

And horse-drawn carts in lanes,

And market days, and little shops,

With latticed window panes.

The children of the newcomers,

What treasures they might see,

The hidden secrets in the lanes

First primroses, bluebells and bird's nests in a tree

This, this is ours, this view of yesterday

Enjoy it while you may,

Laugh at we Cornish Folk,

But in the end you see -

You don't remember our town

The way it used to be!

Garage from Ward Close

Building Ward Close, 1970s

View from Ward Close

Skitchs field

Ward Close

Ward Close

Stratton - Sunday Morning

Stratton, Sunday morning, hear a pheasant call,

Stratton, Sunday morning

Peace lies over all

St Marwenne's Bells at Marhamchurch

If they are heard quite plain

Hear the roaring surf at Widemouth

It is a sign of rain

If east borne wind from Poughill

St Olaf's bells you hear

And crashing waves at Northcott Mouth

Dry weather will be here

Stratton, Sunday morning

St Andrew's bells ring clear

For this is where the heart is

Come storm or balmy weather

Lies all that we hold dear